READY TO RESEARCH...
OUR SOLAR SYSTEM

Written by Vowery Dodd Carlile
Illustrated by Karen Birchak

ISBN 978-1-56644-299-2
© 2008 Educational Impressions, Inc., Hawthorne, NJ

EDUCATIONAL IMPRESSIONS, INC.
Hawthorne, NJ 07507

Printed in the United States of America.

Table of Contents

Introduction

This book was written to teach the process of research to second through fourth graders using the solar system as the topic of learning. The book includes...

- teacher lesson plans;
- steps to completing a research project;
- note-card and organizational-skills template;
- directions on how to cite a resource;
- graphic organizers;
- outline form;
- Bloom's taxonomy lessons;
- product proposal;
- product evaluation;
- product ideas;
- personal-journal template;
- tips on how to do an oral presentation;
- research questions about the solar system;
- background information about the solar system;
- questions dealing with each topic;
- extension activities; and
- a bibliography of resources.

In today's society, it is very important that our students learn how to work independently and that they understand the research process. These lessons are designed to teach the process to second through fourth graders. By the time students are in fifth grade, they should be able to research any topic, cite sources, take notes, organize data, write a paper, produce a product that reflects the research, and present their research and product in an oral presentation. These skills are so important to students for their future in high school and college.

Lesson Plans

Week 1

Day 1: Read the story about Our Solar System, which is found on page 9, to the class. Then discuss it by using the questions on page 11. These questions will help students gain a better understanding of the story.

Day 2: Discuss the fact that some information about the story is more important than the rest. Show students how to break the information down into categories, or topics of interest, about the solar system. See page 12 for examples of categories, or topics.

Make a transparency of the category names or write them on the board. Discuss these categories, pointing out that knowing information about each of the categories would help them understand the solar system better.

Elicit the fact that using note cards to record the important information is a good way to get organized when working on a research topic, in this case the solar system. Elicit what "organized" means. Pass out copies of the solar system story and highlighters. Have students reread the story to find information that will fit into the categories that were listed and to highlight that information.

Days 3–5: Hand out and go over page 13, which explains note-taking, and page 14, which covers summarizing and plagiarism. Duplicate and pass out the sample note cards on page 15. With the students write possible categories at the tops of the cards. Have the students go back to the solar system story, look at their highlighted information, and fill in the information on the note cards.

Week 2

Day 1: Remind students how they took notes about the solar system story last week. Explain that the information came from a resource, or source. List several examples of resources on the board: books, magazines, newspapers, encyclopedias, the internet, TV, radio, etc. Show the students a book and explain that it is a resource. Pass out and use pages 16–20 to teach about bibliographies. Show them where to find the title of the book, the author, where it was published, the publisher, and the copyright date. Explain how to write the information. Use page 19 or 20 to show them an example of the information written into bibliography form. Let them practice this skill using page 21. Page 22 can be used for extra practice in citing sources and taking notes.

Introduce Bloom with pages 23 and 24. Pass out page 25 with sample Bloom questions. Discuss how these questions can be use with the solar system. Page 26 has sample Bloom questions covering the story about the solar system.

Duplicate and distribute page 27. Have students write a Bloom question for each level using the solar system story. After discussing the questions they created, have students put a question on each page of their Bloom Question Book. (See page 28 for directions on how to make the book.) Have students answer each of their questions.

Day 5:   Students continue answering the questions they wrote in their Bloom Book.

Week 3

Day 1:   Use pages 29–32 to make a research journal for each student. Pass out the Student Instructions and explain how the journal is to be used. Then pass out the journals. Explain that the research journal is a way to record their work each day. For example, on the first day of the journal's use, a student might write, "I learned how to use my research journal today." Tomorrow when they learn about graphic organizers, a student might write, "I filled out a graphic organizer for research of the solar system." Repeating what is learned increases retention of the material. Not only can the research journal be used to record what a student learns, it can also reflect the student's feelings about the skill taught that day. Let the students practice making their first entry with today's lesson.

Day 2:   Pass out page 33 to introduce graphic organizers. Explain that the graphic organizer is a way to organize the research in a visual way into fewer papers. Instead of having six or eight note cards, all the information is on one page. It s also a good way to organize a report or story.

Elicit information to help students complete the graphic organizer on page 34. Tell them to use their note cards to fill in the missing information. An example of the filled in organizer is on page 35. (Explain that the graphic organizers may differ.) Explain that there are many formats of graphic organizers and show them the one on page 36.

Leave a few minutes for students to write in their journals about what they learned today.

Day 3: Introduce the outline to the students and show them how to convert the graphic organizer to an outline. Explain that the outline is another, more sophisticated way to organize information. Point out that outlining is a skill that is not usually taught until a student is in fifth grade. Each Roman numeral will hold a category, and the letters will hold details to support the category. Cardinal numbers are then used for more specific details. Outlines are also a good way to learn about main idea and details. Page 37 contains a completed outline for the solar system story. Page 38 provides a template for an outline. (Explain that the outlines may differ.)

Days 4–5: Give each student one of the solar system stories found on pages 39–75. Some students may have to be given the same story depending on the size of the group. Let them practice note-taking, using a separate note card for each category. You may want to make a list of categories for the note cards and put them on the board.

Allow students time to write in their journals.

There are questions after each solar system story that can be used during the research process; they can also provide comprehension feedback as to the students' understanding of the story. There are also creative-thinking activities at the end of the book which will provide opportunities to use the knowledge learned from the research and to perform at a higher level.

Week 4

Day 1: The students are now ready to choose their own solar system topic and to do an independent research project using the skills they have practiced. Have students choose a topic they would like to research. Take them to the library and help them find a book about their topic. One of the sources for their research may be the story found in this book. Have them use one or two other sources.

Use the instructions on pages 78–80 to make a research pouch for each student. These pouches will help them keep their research project in order.

Make a copy of Steps for Completing a Research Project found on page 81 for each student. Explain that they will be using the same skills that they have practiced, except that they will have chosen a topic of interest to them and will use at least one source in addition to the story in the book. Have them check off each task as it is completed.

Students should be able to choose their own topic. Be sure to help them narrow down their topic to be workable.

Days 2–5: Follow the Steps to Completing a Research Project to finish the unit. You may choose to do a product. See pages 82–84 for examples, planning sheets, and evaluations for projects.

Week 5

Days 1–5: Continue with the research project. When the project is completed, have students present their findings to the class in an oral presentation. Hand out and discuss the Oral Presentation Tips on page 85 to help students prepare for their presentations.

You might want to set up a Solar System Fair. Invite other classes or parents to the fair and have students stand behind their desk or behind a table with their projects spread out in front of them. Let the students tell about their projects as guests walk by. Students need to have more opportunities to present orally. This will make it easier and more comfortable as they get older. Life is full of presentations!

Our Solar System

A solar system is made up of a star, the planets and their moons and all the other bodies, such as dwarf planets, asteroids, comets and meteoroids, that revolve around it. Our solar system began more than four billion years ago. Gases came together, forming the sun, the planets and the other bodies. Our solar system stretches across space for billions of miles.

The star that we call the sun is the center of our solar system. The sun is the only body in our solar system to give off light of its own. The sun's light and heat make life on Earth possible. The sun is one of the billions of stars in the Milky Way Galaxy. Scientists believe there are about 100 billion stars in the Milky Way.

The large bodies that revolve around the sun, including Earth, are called planets. Planets reflect the light of the sun but do not give off any light of their own. There are eight known planets. In order of their distance from the sun they are Mercury, Venus, Earth, Mars, Jupiter, Saturn, Uranus, and Neptune. Each planet takes a different path. These paths are called orbits. Most of the planets have elliptical, or oval, orbits.

Until recently scientists believed there were nine planets. Pluto, which was discovered in 1848, was considered a planet for a long time. In 2006 the International Astronomical Union issued a definition of *planet* and reclassified Pluto as a dwarf planet. Eris, which was first discovered in 2003, and the asteroid Ceres were also classified as dwarf planets. In the future there are sure to be others.

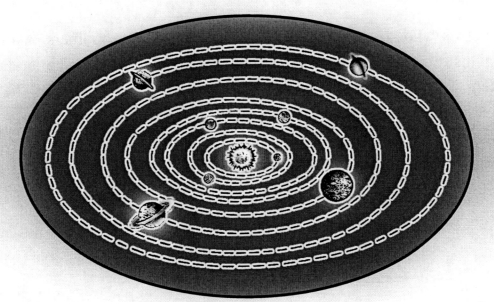

As the planets revolve around the sun, they spin like a top. This spinning motion is called rotation. The planets rotate around an imaginary line called an axis. The axis goes through the middle of the planet. Most planets, Earth included, tilt on their axis.

The planets are made from different materials. The four inner planets—those closest to the sun—are made mostly of rock and metal. They have few or no moons. The four outer planets are giant balls of gas. These huge planets have many moons. Of course, each planet has its own unique characteristics.

Asteroids are odd-shaped pieces of rock. There are many different shapes and sizes. Some are only a few hundred feet in diameter. Others are hundreds of miles wide. Many asteroids are found in an area between Mars and Jupiter. In fact, this area is often called the Asteroid Belt. Sometimes an asteroid is pulled out of its orbit by the gravity of a planet. When that happens, the asteroid may become a moon of that planet!

Comets also orbit the sun. They are made up of ice, dust and gas. Many comets have a long, glowing tail that shines brightly as the comet approaches the sun. However, a comet can sometimes loose its tail.

Small chunks of rock and metal that have broken off from asteroids and comets, called meteoroids, circle the sun too. Most are about the size of a pebble, but some are much larger. When a meteoroid falls into Earth's atmosphere, we call it a meteor. Most meteors burn up before they hit Earth. If any part of it actually hits Earth, we call it a meteorite. When a meteorite hits a planet, it forms a hole called a crater.

Scientists who study the solar system are called astronomers. Astronomers use special instruments called telescopes to study the planets and other bodies in our solar system. With these instruments they can see craters on the moon, the rings of Saturn, the moons of Jupiter and much more. They also use these instruments to study other stars in the Milky Way Galaxy.

Even though astronomers know a lot about our solar system, there are many discoveries yet to be made.

Solar System Discussion Questions

1. What is meant by a solar system? What are the bodies in our solar system?

_____

_____

_____

2. What is the center of our solar system?

_____

_____

_____

3. Name the planets and describe their movements.

_____

_____

_____

4. What is a comet? Describe it.

_____

_____

_____

5. What is an asteroid?

_____

_____

_____

6. What is an astronomer? Which is the most important instrument of an astronomer? Explain your answer.

_____

_____

_____

Possible Categories
for Note Cards

Directions: Use these or other categories for your note cards. Put one category name on each note card. Make sure a different color of note card is used for each source.

Make-up

Size

Special Characteristics

Moons

Rotation and Revolution Periods

Weather

Unique Features

Note Cards and Organization

Use color-coded note cards if possible. There are large, lined cards made for elementary students. Put all the information from one source on cards of the same color. For example, all pink cards may refer to a certain book; all blue cards may come from an internet source; all white cards come from a magazine source; etc. You may use a colored dot, etc., if you cannot find colored cards.

Make sure the first card of a color has the resource information. (See card No. 1.) Each note card should have a title or category describing what that card is about. (See Card No. 2.)

Card No. 1

Kim, Herbert. Comets. New York: William Morrow & Co., 1957.

Card No. 2

Comet
• Made of...
    rock
    ice
    dust
• Long, glowing tail

Summarizing

To **summarize** is to pick out the important points of information. You then write (or say) them in a few words.

Text in Story:

The large bodies that revolve around the sun, including Earth, are called planets. Planets reflect the light of the sun but do not give off any light of their own. There are eight known planets. In order of their distance from the sun they are Mercury, Venus, Earth, Mars, Jupiter, Saturn, Uranus, and Neptune. Each planet takes a different path. These paths are called orbits. Most of the planets have elliptical, or oval, orbits.

Summary for Note Card:

Planets

Revolve around sun   No light of own

Closest to farthest from from sun:

   Mercury, Venus, Earth, Mars, Jupiter, Saturn, Uranus, Neptune

Elliptical orbits

Plagiarism

When someone writes a report and uses the exact words from the author of the source, it is called plagiarism. **The following is an example of plagiarism.**

The large bodies that revolve around the sun, including Earth, are called planets. Planets reflect the light of the sun but do not give off any light of their own. There are eight known planets. In order of their distance from the sun they are Mercury, Venus, Earth, Mars, Jupiter, Saturn, Uranus, and Neptune. Each planet takes a different path. These paths are called orbits. Most of the planets have elliptical, or oval, orbits.

Here is the same information put into the student's own words.

Eight planets—Mercury, Venus, Earth, Mars, Jupiter, Saturn, Uranus, and Neptune—revolve around the sun in elliptical paths called orbits. Mercury is the closest planet to the sun, and Neptune is the farthest. The planets reflect the light of the sun, but the sun is the only body in the solar system to give off its own light.

Bibliographies

A **bibliography** is a list of books and other sources of information. There are two main reasons to have a bibliography. First of all, it shows the research an author has done in preparing the work. It also tells readers where they can look if they want more information on the subject.

Each entry includes important information:

- Title of the Book
- Author's Name
- Name of Publisher
- Publication Date (Use the copyright date.)

Entries are listed in alphabetical order. Alphabetical order is based on the first important word in the entry. Usually, that will be the author's last name. If an entry begins with a title, do not use the words "A," "An," or "The" to put the entries in order.

Bibliographies should be easy to read. Put a line space between each entry. Also, indent all lines in an entry except the first.

General Rules

Begin each entry at the left margin.

Indent all lines of an entry except the first.

Authors' names are written last name first. (If there are more than one author, write the first author last name first and the others in normal order: first name and then last name.)

If there are more than one author, write them in the same order as on the title page.

Alphabetize by the first important word in the entry. (Do not use "A," "An," or "The.")

Book and magazine titles should be printed in italics or underlined.

Tiles of articles in magazines are put in quotation marks.

Each entry should end with a period.

Skip a line between each entry.

Title Page

The information you need for the bibliography will be found
on the title page and its reverse side.

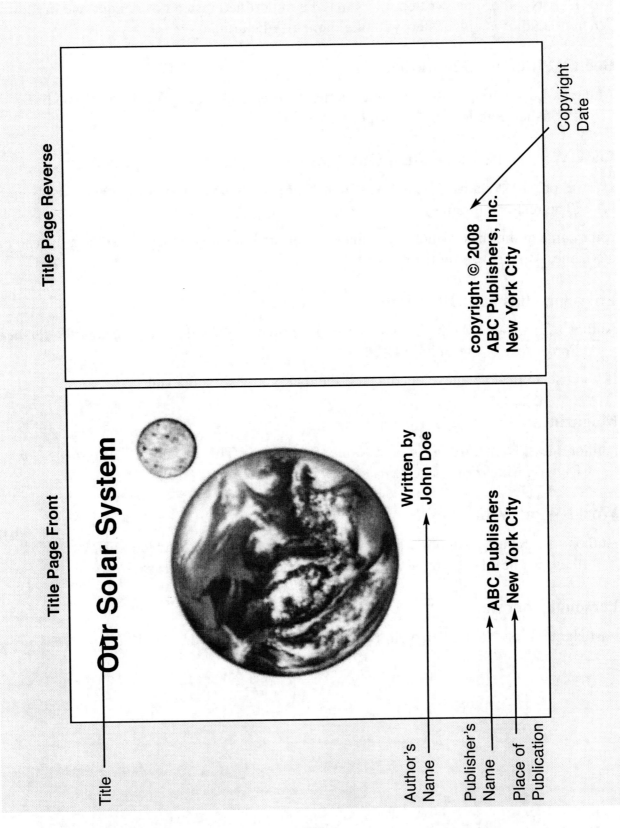

Title Page Reverse

Copyright Date

copyright © 2008
ABC Publishers, Inc.
New York City

Title Page Front

Our Solar System

Title

Written by
John Doe

Author's Name

ABC Publishers
New York City

Publisher's Name

Place of Publication

Bibliography Formats

Follow the appropriate format for each type of resource. Be sure to notice the punctuation as well as the order of the information.

NOTE: If typed or handwritten, titles may be underlined instead of being done in italics. When no author is given, start with the name of the article.

Book Written by One Author:

Author's Last Name, Author's First Name. *Title of Book.* City Where Published: Publisher, Publication/Copyright Date.

Book Written by More Than One Author:

1st Author's Last Name, 1st Author's First Name, and 2nd Author's First and Last Name. (The rest is the same.)

If the same author has written more than one of the books, you may use a dash instead of the name. Alphabetize by the book title.

Encyclopedias and Other Reference Books:

Author's Last Name, Author's First Name (If known). "Title of Article." *Title of Reference Book.* Year of the Edition Used.

If you use an on-line encyclopedia, add the date you visited the site.

Magazines:

Author's Last Name, Author's First Name (If known). "Title of Article." *Magazine Name.* Date on Magazine: page(s).

World Wide Web:

Author's Last Name, Author's First Name (If known). "Title of Article." *Title of Work* (if there is one). Date you visited the site. <complete http address>.

Personal Interview:

Last Name, First Name. Personal Interview. Date Interviewed.

Bibliography: Simplified Version

When creating a bibliography, you must follow certain formats. The information should be given in a certain order. Also, it is important to use correct punctuation.

Note: Titles in italics may be underlined instead.

Book

Author's Last Name, Author's First Name. *Title of Book*. Where Published: Publisher, Year of Publication.

Encyclopedia

"Subject." Name of Encyclopedia, Year of Publication. Page Numbers.

Encyclopedia on CD-ROM

"Subject." Name of Encyclopedia, Year of Publication. CD-ROM.

Online Encyclopedia

"Subject." Name of Encyclopedia, Date you visited the site. Online.

Sample Bibliography

Books

Simon, Seymour. *Stars.* New York: Mulberry Paperback Books, 1986.

Zim, Herbert. *Comets.* New York: William Morrow and Company, 1957.

Magazine

Dorren, Karen. "Stars." *National Geographic.* December 1999: pages 70–75.

Encyclopedia

"Comets." *Encyclopaedia Britannica.* 2005. CD-ROM.

World Wide Web

"Solar System." 1/23/2007. http://www.bbc.co.uk/science/space/solarsystem/

Interview

Andrews, Ty. Personal Interview. December 2005.

Note: If you are writing by hand or typing, underline instead of using italics.

Resources

We use several different kinds of **resources** when doing research. Books, magazines, journals, encyclopedias, newspapers, the internet, and personal interviews are all possible resources, or sources of information. Each type of resource has its own set of rules.

Use this sheet to practice citing, or giving information about, sources.

Title of Book: _____

Author: _____

Where it was Published: _____

Publisher: _____

Copyright Date: _____

Check your Bibliography Format Sheet. Write down the information in the correct order. Check your punctuation.

_____

_____

_____

_____

_____

_____

Source-Information and Note-Card Template

Title of Book: _____

Author: _____

Where It Was Published: _____

Publisher: _____

Copyright Date: _____

Author (last name first). *Title of Book*. Where It Was published: Publisher,
   Copyright Date.

_____

_____

_____

Category or topic: _____

Notes: _____

_____

_____

_____

_____

_____

_____

_____

_____

Levels of Bloom's Taxonomy

Benjamin Bloom divided educational questions into six main categories; they are knowledge, comprehension, application, analysis, synthesis and evaluation. The last four levels promote critical and creative thinking.

Level	_Skill Involved_
Knowledge:	simple recall
Comprehension:	understanding of the material
Application:	applying learned information to a new situation
Analysis:	the breaking down of learned knowledge into small parts
Synthesis:	creating something new and original from the acquired knowledge
Evaluation:	making a judgment and backing it up

Question Cues

The following verbs can help in writing Bloom questions.

Knowledge:　　　　　　　　list, know, define, relate, repeat, recall, specify, tell, name

Comprehension:　　　　　recognize, restate, explain, describe, summarize, express, review, discuss, identify, locate, report, retell

Application:　　　　　　　demonstrate, interview, simulate, dramatize, experiment, show, use, employ, operate, exhibit, apply, calculate, solve, illustrate

Analysis:　　　　　　　　compare, examine, categorize, group, test, inventory, probe, analyze, discover, arrange, organize, contrast, classify, survey

Synthesis:　　　　　　　plan, develop, invent, predict, propose, produce, arrange, formulate, construct, incorporate, originate, create, prepare, design, set up

Evaluation:　　　　　　value, recommend, evaluate, criticize, estimate, decide, conclude, predict, judge, compare, rate, measure, select, infer

Bloom Questions

Knowledge

    1. List the parts of _____.

    2. Define how to _____.

    3. What does _____ mean?

Comprehension

    1. Describe how to _____.

    2. Explain how _____ happened.

    3. Locate where _____ is found.

Application

    1. Demonstrate how to _____.

    2. Tell how to operate a _____.

    3. Dramatize how _____ is different today.

Analysis

    1. Compare and contrast _____ and _____.

    2. How would you test _____?

    3. Organize _____ and test it.

Synthesis

    1. Plan a new way to _____.

    2. Create a new _____. Explain it.

    3. Design a way to _____.

Evaluation

    1. Judge the usefulness of _____.

    2. Predict how _____ may change _____.

    3. Recommend _____ to someone.

Examples of Bloom Questions
About Our Solar System

Knowledge: 1. How many planets are in our solar system?

                   2. What is an asteroid?

Comprehension: 1. Explain what an orbit is.

                   2. Describe a astronomer's job.

Application: 1. Pretend to interview an astronomer. What three questions would you ask him/her?

                   2. Classify the planets by their size, their distance from the sun and their physical make-up.

Analysis: 1. Explain the difference between an asteroid and a meteor.

                   2. Discuss the difference between a planet's rotating and revolving.

Synthesis: 1. Suppose you were asked to change our solar system. What would you change and why?

                   2. Create another planet for our solar system. Describe it and give it a name.

Evaluation: 1. Would you like to travel into space? Why or why not?

                   2. Recommend to an alien why the Earth is a good place to live.

Template for Bloom Questions

Knowledge

_____

_____

Comprehension

_____

_____

Application

_____

_____

Analysis

_____

_____

Synthesis

_____

_____

Evaluation

_____

_____

Bloom Book

Materials:

3 sheets of 8½" x 11" unlined construction paper, each a different color
Stapler
Ruler

Instructions:

Lay down one sheet of colored paper. Place a sheet of another color on top of that one 1½ inches from the top. Do the same with the third sheet of colored paper, placing it 1½ inches from the top of the second sheet. Now from the bottom, fold up each sheet to create another 1½-inch section until you get the last sheet folded up. Staple along the edge of the bottom. On each 1½-inch section, have students write a Bloom Question. From top to bottom the questions should be on the following levels: Knowledge, Comprehension, Application, Analysis, Synthesis, and Evaluation. Put the answer under the flap that the question is on. The evaluation question can be answered on the back of the bottom section.

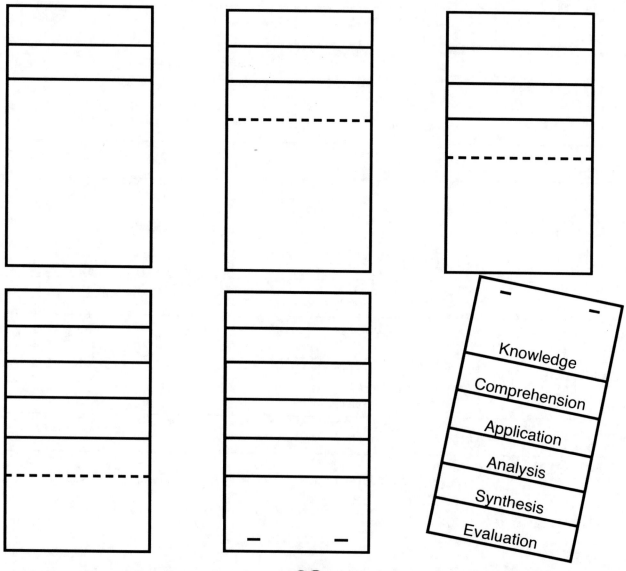

Research Journals:
Teacher Directions

Making the Journal:

Do the following for EACH journal.

1. Copy the sheet with the front and back cover sheets onto construction paper or oak tag.

2. Cut the sheet in half so that you have both the front cover and the back cover.

3. Make ten copies of the journal-entry sheet.

4. Cut the journal-entry sheets apart so that you have twenty pages.

5. Assemble the book.

6. Staple in two places along the side.

Research Journals:
Student Instructions

Your research journal is a way for you to record your work every day. For example, today you might write in your journal, "Today I learned how to write in my research journal."

Things to Include in Your Journal Research:

• Skill(s) you learned in class

• What you feel about the day's lesson

• Books you read

• Other sources you used

• Did you go to the library?

• Did you use a computer?

My Journal

by

_____

Date _____

What I did today:

_____

_____

_____

_____

What I learned new today:

_____

_____

_____

_____

_____

Date _____

What I did today:

_____

_____

_____

_____

What I learned new today:

_____

_____

_____

_____

_____

Graphic Organizers

A good tool to help you organize your notes is a graphic organizer. No matter what the pattern, a graphic organizer helps you to divide the topic into categories and to summarize the important information. You can use the graphic organizer as a guide when you write your report.

NOTE: Organizers may vary. This is one example.

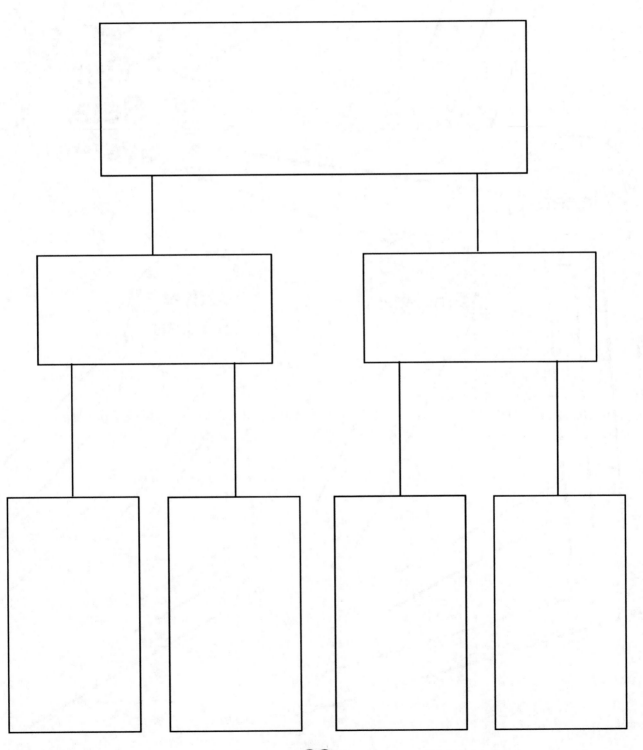

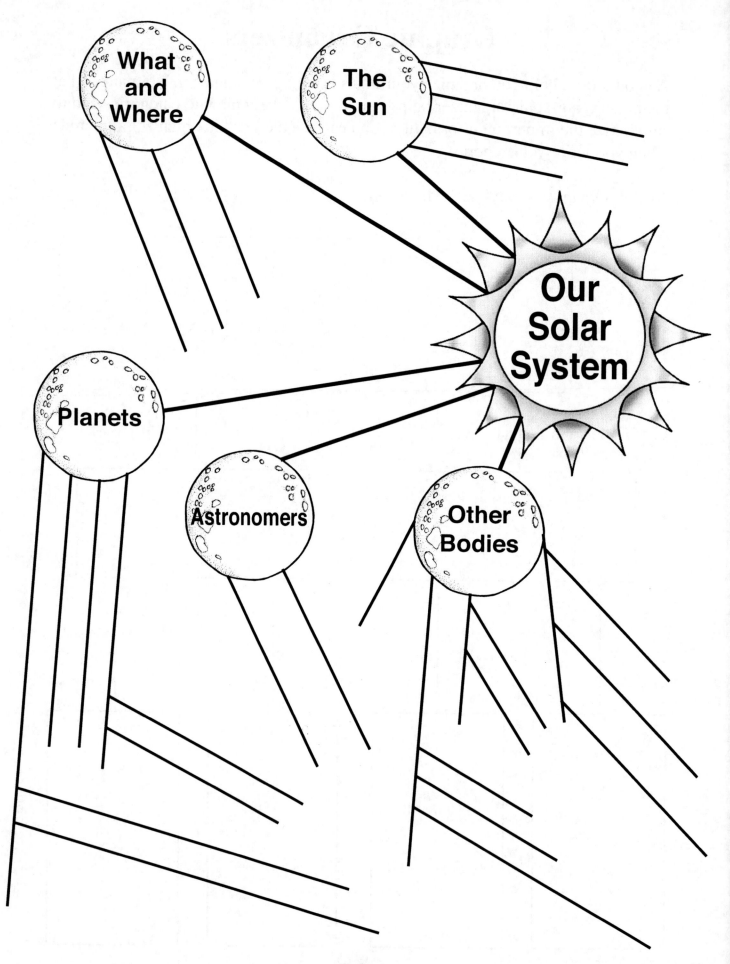

What
and
Where

The
Sun

Our
Solar
System

Planets

Astronomers

Other
Bodies

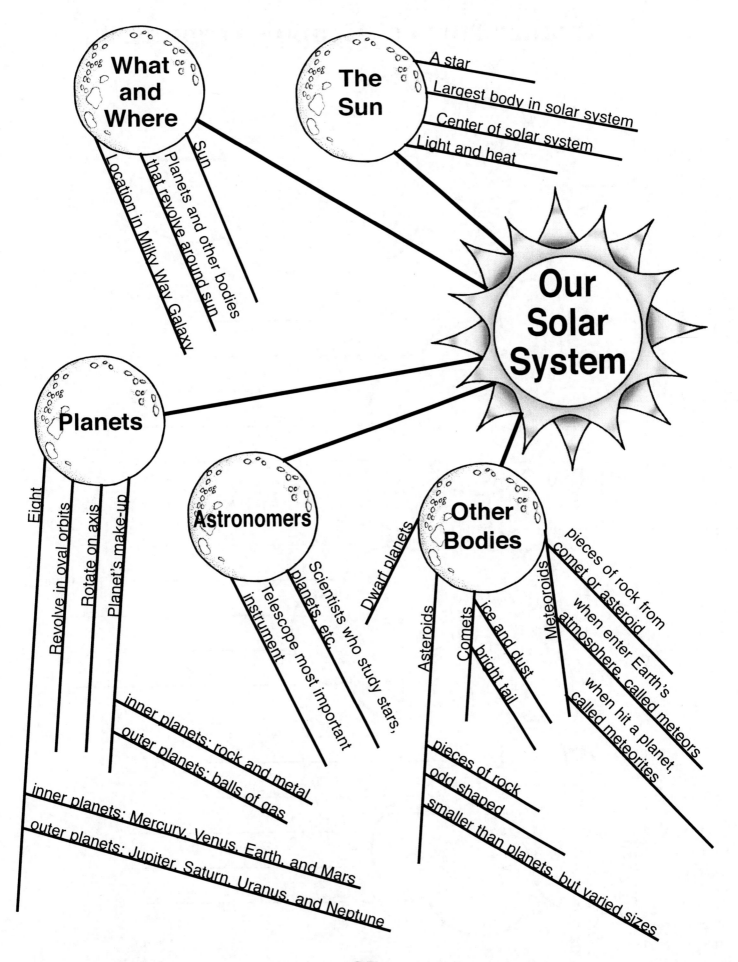

Our Solar System

What and Where
- Sun
- Planets and other bodies that revolve around sun
- Location in Milky Way Galaxy

The Sun
- A star
- Largest body in solar system
- Center of solar system
- Light and heat

Planets
- Eight
- Revolve in oval orbits
- Rotate on axis
- Planet's make-up
  - inner planets: rock and metal
  - outer planets: balls of gas
  - inner planets: Mercury, Venus, Earth, and Mars
  - outer planets: Jupiter, Saturn, Uranus, and Neptune

Astronomers
- Scientists who study stars, planets, etc.
- Telescope most important instrument

Other Bodies
- Dwarf planets
- Asteroids
  - pieces of rock
  - odd shaped
  - smaller than planets, but varied sizes
- Comets
  - ice and dust
  - bright tail
- Meteoroids
  - pieces of rock from comet or asteroid
  - when enter Earth's atmosphere, called meteors
  - when hit a planet, called meteorites

Another Form of Graphic Organizer

_____
_____
_____
_____

_____
_____
_____
_____

_____
_____
_____
_____

OUR SOLAR SYSTEM

I. What and Where

    A. Sun

    B. Planets and other bodies that revolve around sun

    C. Location in Milky Way Galaxy

II. Sun

    A. A star

    B. Largest body in solar system

    C. Center of solar system

    D. Light and heat

III. Planets

    A. Eight

        1. inner planets: Mercury, Venus, Earth, and Mars

        2. outer planets: Jupiter, Saturn, Uranus, and Neptune

    B. Revolve in oval orbits

    C. Rotate on axis

    D. Planets' make-up

        1. inner planets: rock & metal

        2. outer planets: balls of gas

IV. Other Bodies

    A. Dwarf planets

    B. Asteroids

        1. pieces of rock

        2. odd shaped

        3. smaller than planets, but varied sizes

    C. Comets

        1. ice and dust

        2. bright tail

    D. Meteoroids

        1. pieces of rock from comet or asteroid

        2. when enter Earth's atmosphere, called meteors

        3. when hit a planet, called meteorites

V. Astronomers

    A. Scientists who study stars, planets, etc.

    B. Telescope most important instrument

OUR SOLAR SYSTEM

I. _____
   A. _____
   B. _____
   C. _____

II. _____
   A. _____
   B. _____
   C. _____
   D. _____

III. _____
   A. _____
      1. _____
      2. _____
   B. _____
   C. _____
   D. _____
      1. _____
      2. _____

IV. _____
   A. _____
   B. _____
      1. _____
      2. _____
      3. _____
   C _____
      1. _____
      2. _____
   D. _____
      1. _____
      2. _____
      3. _____

V. _____
   A. _____
   B. _____

Solar System Stories

The Sun

The sun is a star. It is one of about 100 billion stars in the Milky Way Galaxy. At about 93 million miles away from Earth, the sun is the closest star to our planet. Naturally, it is the one we know the most about.

The sun is the most important body in our solar system. The planets and all of the other bodies in our solar system revolve around it. It is the sun's gravity that keeps all of them in orbit. Because it is a star, the sun gives off its own light. It is the only body in our solar system that does.

The sun is by far the largest object in our solar system. It is about 864,000 miles around. This is ten times larger than the diameter of Jupiter, the next largest object. If the sun were hollow, over a million Earths would fit inside it! However, our sun is really a medium-sized star. Many stars are larger than our sun.

The sun is made mostly of two gases—about 71% hydrogen and about 21% helium. The two gases combine to make energy, which comes to us in form of heat and light. The sun's temperature at its core ranges from about 10 million degrees Fahrenheit to over 20 million degrees! The temperature at the surface is about 10,000 degrees Fahrenheit.

Although our sun is just a medium-sized star, it is the most important star to us on Earth! It gives us just the right amount of heat and light. If it weren't for the sun's heat, Earth would be a cold, barren place. Light from the sun is needed in order for our plants to grow. Without plants, animals that eat those plants would not survive. Animals that eat those plant-eaters would not survive either.

The sun affects climate on Earth. Although there are other factors, generally, the more direct the sun's rays, the warmer the climate. At the equator the sun's rays hit directly all of the time. That is why it is always hot at the equator. When the sun's rays hit at an angle, they are not as strong. They are least intense near the poles. That is why it is always cold at the poles.

The sun is also responsible for changes in our weather. It warms the air around us. It also warms the oceans and other bodies of water. The sun evaporates some of the water, producing clouds. Out of the clouds come the rain and snow that provide moisture for our planet Earth.

A star does not last forever. Because the sun is a star, it will eventually burn itself out. But we don't have to worry about that! According to astronomers, the sun has about 7 billion years to go. Of course this is a very, very long time. When the sun does begin to run out of hydrogen, it will swell and become a giant red star. It will then shed its outer layers and become a white dwarf, eventually not giving off any heat or light.

The sun is very important to us. Without the sun, there would be no life on Earth!

The Sun Discussion Questions

1. What is the sun? Explain its importance in the solar system.

_____

_____

_____

2. Describe the sun's make-up.

_____

_____

_____

3. How far from Earth is the sun?

_____

_____

_____

4. Describe how the sun affects the weather on Earth.

_____

_____

_____

5. What benefits does the sun provide Earth? What would Earth's future be if there were no sun? Explain your answer.

_____

_____

_____

6. Explain a star's life.

_____

_____

_____

Mercury

Mercury was named after the messenger god in ancient Roman mythology. At 36,000,000 miles away, Mercury is the closest planet to the sun. The sunny side of Mercury is very hot, about 800 degrees Fahrenheit. On the the dark side of the planet, however, the temperature can plunge to -280 degrees.

Mercury is also the smallest planet in our solar system. It is only about 3,030 miles in diameter. It has no moons.

Because Mercury is so close to the sun, it has a relatively short year. Its year—the time it takes to orbit the sun—is only about 88 Earth-days long. However, Mercury rotates very slowly on its axis; therefore, its day lasts almost 59 Earth days! This combination has an amazing effect: any point on Mercury will have daytime (face the sun) for one Mercurian year and nighttime (face away from the sun) for one Mercurian year! Astronauts on Mercury would see the sunrise only every 176 Earth days!

Pictures from the spacecraft *Mariner 10* showed that Mercury's surface looks a lot like that of the moon, full of craters and basins. These craters and basins were caused by collisions with comets and asteroids. The biggest basin on Mercury is about 800 miles across. Called Caloris Basin, it is one of the largest impact craters in the solar system. The collision that made this basin must have been very powerful because the other side of Mercury has large rocky ridges that were caused by shock waves from the event.

Mercury has a huge iron core, which gives it its magnetic field. The outer surface of the planet is made of molten rock, or lava. Mercury also has wrinkles. These were made when the planet formed. After the planet cooled, its core shrank. This caused the crust to buckle, pushing up the giant wrinkles.

Due to Mercury's surface and closeness to the sun, it has no wind, rain or clouds. Mercury cannot support life.

Mercury Discussion Questions

1. Describe Mercury's size and temperature.

_____

_____

_____

2. Explain why Mercury is so hot.

_____

_____

_____

3. Why are there craters on Mercury? Tell about Caloris Basin.

_____

_____

_____

4. Why is Mercury's day length so different from that of Earth?

_____

_____

_____

5. How long does it take for Mercury to revolve around the sun?

_____

_____

_____

6. Why, do you think, was the planet named after the Roman god Mercury?

_____

_____

_____

Venus

Venus, the second planet from the sun, was named after the ancient Roman mythological goddess of love. After the moon, Venus is the brightest object in our night sky. Because Venus is so bright at dawn and dusk, it is sometimes called the "morning star" or the "evening star." Venus is about 7,520 miles in diameter. That is a little smaller than our planet Earth. Like Mercury, Venus has no moons.

Venus is the hottest planet in our solar system—even hotter than Mercury. The reason it is so hot is that it has a very thick atmosphere, which is composed mostly of carbon dioxide. Its clouds contain sulfuric acid. The sun's rays are able to penetrate the atmosphere, but the clouds stop the heat from getting back out. That is why the surface of Venus is so hot—about 880 degrees Fahrenheit. This is called the greenhouse effect: the sun's heat can get in, but cannot get out.

Several spacecrafts have mapped the surface of Venus using radar. The planet's surface is made up of volcanoes and lava flows. Fewer craters were found on Venus than on any other planet. Astronomers think this is because Venus still has active volcanoes that flow and fill the old craters with lava or molten rock.

Even though few craters have been found on Venus, Venus has the biggest and best preserved crater in our solar system. It is named Mead Crater and is about 175 miles in diameter. Mead Crater looks like any other volcanic crater until the rings of debris surrounding the crater are observed. This tells us that the crater was most likely caused by a meteor that hit the planet.

There are several unique and interesting features about Venus. For instance, Venus's day is longer than its year! The planet orbits the sun once every 225 Earth days. However, Venus rotates on its axis extremely slowly. It takes about 243 Earth days for Venus to rotate once.

Another interesting fact about Venus is that it rotates clockwise. The other planets, with the possible exception of Uranus, rotate in a counterclockwise direction. This causes the sun to rise in the west and set in the east.

Because of its harsh atmosphere, Venus cannot support life.

Venus Discussion Questions

1. Describe Venus.

_____

_____

_____

2. Why is Venus the hottest planet in our solar system? Why is this surprising?

_____

_____

_____

3. What do scientists think might be the reason there are few craters on Venus?

_____

_____

_____

4. What is unusual about the length of a day on Venus?

_____

_____

_____

5. Why does the sun set in the east and not in the west like on Earth?

_____

_____

_____

6. How do we know as much as we do about Venus?

_____

_____

_____

Earth

Earth is the third planet from the sun. Seen from space it looks blue. The Earth is about 7,926 miles around. It is the largest of the four small rocky planets and the fifth largest planet in the solar system. Earth has one moon. It is the only planet in our solar system with water in all three forms: solid, liquid and vapor. Earth appears to be the only planet that can support life.

Earth has three layers: the center, or core; the middle, called the mantle; and the upper layer, called the crust. The core is made of iron and nickel. The mantle is made up of molten rock. The upper layer, or crust, is made up of different kinds of rocks. About 24% of Earth's crust is covered with mountains.

About 71% of Earth's crust is covered by a huge body of water called the ocean. Although it is really one body of water, we divide the ocean into separate areas. The names we give to the great oceans are the Pacific Ocean, the Atlantic Ocean, the Indian Ocean, Arctic Ocean and the Southern Ocean, or Antarctic. Some scientists consider the Southern Ocean to be the southern portions of the Pacific, Atlantic and Indian oceans.

The Earth's atmosphere is made up of mostly nitrogen and oxygen with traces of water vapor and other gases. This atmosphere traps some of the heat from the sun and allows some to escape back into space. Earth's weather takes place in the first seven miles of its atmosphere. Temperatures on the planet range from -127 to 136 degrees Fahrenheit. Of course, these are the extremes.

Earth rotates on its axis once about every 24 hours— every 23 hours and 56 minutes to be exact. This is an Earth day. It takes the Earth 365.25 Earth days to revolve around the sun. This is an Earth year.

Earth's rotation on its axis is what causes day and night. The part of Earth that faces the sun has daytime. The part of Earth that is faces away from the sun has nighttime.

Earth's revolution and tilt cause the different seasons. For instance, around June 21, the North Pole tilts more towards the sun, so it is summer in the northern hemisphere. The opposite is true in the southern hemisphere, so it is winter there. Around December 21, the North Pole tilts away from the sun, so it is winter in the northern hemisphere and summer in the southern hemisphere. In spring and fall both hemispheres get about the same amount of energy from the sun. The sun always hits directly in regions around the equator, so it stays warm there year round.

Earth is a beautiful planet and the only known planet in our solar system that can support life.

Earth Discussion Questions

1. In your opinion, what is the most special thing about the planet Earth?

_____

_____

_____

2. Describe Earth's layers.

_____

_____

_____

3. Which two gases make up most of Earth's atmosphere?

_____

_____

_____

4. Explain why we have different seasons.

_____

_____

_____

5. Name the oceans.

_____

_____

_____

6. What are the lengths of a day and a year on Earth? How are they determined?

_____

_____

_____

© Educational Impressions, Inc.   **51**   *Ready to Research...Our Solar System*

Mars

Mars was named after the ancient Roman mythological god of war. It is the fourth planet from the sun. Although only about half its size—Mars is about 4,215 miles in diameter—it is the planet most like our planet Earth. Like Earth, Mars has a thin crust. Its surface is dry and rocky and there are polar ice caps and water channels. Mars is known as the red planet because of the rusty orange rocks and red sand of its surface. Mars has two moons.

The length of a day on Mars is about the same as an Earth day. Mars rotates on its axis every 24 hours and 37 minutes in Earth time. Of course, a year on Mars is much longer. It takes 687 Earth days for Mars to make a trip around the sun once.

Scientists think that when Mars was young, it may have supported some form of life. However, spacecraft have found no signs of life today. This is probably due to its harsh environment. Mars is now a cold, desert planet. During the day the temperature on Mars may rise to 82 degrees Fahrenheit, but it drops to -190 degrees at night.

The southern part of the planet has many craters. It also has a giant canyon system. This system stretches about 3,100 miles along the equator with an average depth of 9.5 miles.

The northern side of Mars is smooth and flat. It appears to have had large lakes and an ocean at one time. It also has a volcano that is 50 times larger than any on Earth. This volcano is named Olympus Mons. It is about 17 miles high and 435 miles across. It has been extinct for many years.

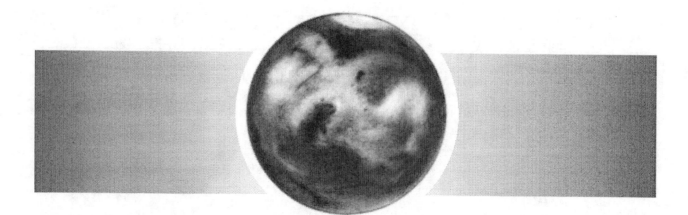

Mars has very unpredictable weather. It can change very quickly. Temperatures can drop 20 degrees in a matter of minutes. A tornado was observed on the planet that was almost 13 miles high. It caused much damage to the barren surface.

Because Mars is so close to the Earth, it is the most studied planet—except, of course, for Earth—in our solar system. Someday astronauts may even explore Mars and walk on its surface like they did on our moon!

Mars Discussion Questions

1. How is Mars like Earth?

_____

_____

_____

2. What was found on Mars to make scientists think there may have been life on Mars at one time?

_____

_____

_____

3. Explain why Mars is called the red planet.

_____

_____

_____

4. Describe the southern half of Mars.

_____

_____

_____

5. Describe the northern half of Mars.

_____

_____

_____

6. What are the lengths of a day and a year on Mars in Earth time?

_____

_____

_____

Jupiter

Jupiter was named for the ancient Roman mythological ruler of the gods. It is the fifth planet from the sun. After the sun, Jupiter is the largest body in our solar system. It is almost 89,000 miles around. This is more than eleven times the diameter of our planet Earth! Jupiter has four large moons and many smaller ones.

Scientists can see with the aid of a telescope that Jupiter has beautiful clouds. The bright colors in Jupiter's clouds are caused by interactions of various gases. Jupiter is the third brightest object in the night sky. Only our moon and Venus are brighter.

Jupiter's atmosphere is composed of gases, about 90% hydrogen and 10% helium. The planet has no solid surface. Beneath the top layer of gas is a middle layer of liquid metal. In the center of the planet is believed to be a small, rocky core that is three times hotter than the sun.

Jupiter has distinct bands that encircle the planet. These are caused by high-speed winds. Jupiter also has faint, dark rings made of tiny pieces of rock and dust.

It takes less than 10 Earth hours for Jupiter to rotate on its axis! Because it rotates so quickly, winds blow at around 300 miles an hour. Another result of its quick rotation is that the planet appears to be slightly flattened at the poles and bulging at the equator.

The high winds combined with heat from the core cause great storms. These storms can last for years or even centuries. One such storm, known as the Great Red Spot, has been seen for at least 300 years. This storm is more than twice the size of Earth. Why this storm has lasted so long is a mystery.

A Jovian year is equal to 11.9 Earth years. In other words, it takes Jupiter about 11.9 Earth years to orbit the sun once. Because Jupiter is only slightly tilted on its axis, there are no seasons in a Jovian year.

Jupiter is believed to have more moons than any other planet in our solar system. Scientists have found at least 63 although most are very small. The four largest moons were first discovered by the scientist Galileo in 1610 using an early telescope. The many smaller moons were probably asteroids that came too close to the planet and were drawn into Jupiter's strong magnetic field. There is something very strange about these smaller moons: they travel opposite to the big ones.

There are many mysteries yet to be discovered about Jupiter. Using unmanned spacecraft, scientists learn more all the time. The one thing is that is known for sure, however, is that life cannot be supported on the huge ball of gas we call Jupiter!

Jupiter Discussion Questions

1. Compare Jupiter in size to the other objects in our solar system.

_____

_____

_____

2. What is the length of a day on Jupiter?

_____

_____

_____

3. What is the length of a year on Jupiter? Why are there no seasons?

_____

_____

_____

4. What is the Great Red Spot?

_____

_____

_____

5. Why does Jupiter have beautiful colors?

_____

_____

_____

6. Explain why Jupiter has so many moons.

_____

_____

_____

Saturn

Saturn was named after the god of agriculture in the mythology of the ancient Romans. It is the sixth planet from the sun and the second largest planet in the solar system. It is almost 75,000 miles in diameter. Saturn is known as the ringed planet because of its beautiful rings. Even though some of the other planets have rings, Saturn's rings are the most magnificent. They are very wide and very thin.

Saturn's rings have letter names. They are D, C, B, A, F, G, and E. Rings D to A are the four main rings. D is closest to the planet and is followed by C and B. Between B and A is a large space of about 2,900 miles. The first four rings were discovered by the scientist Galileo in 1610 using an early telescope. The last three rings—F, G, and E—are fainter and narrower and were not discovered until much later.

Through the voyages of spaceships, it has been discovered that Saturn's rings are made up of chunks of ice. These chunks are believed to be moons that collided and shattered into thousands of pieces. Millions of years from now Saturn's rings will be gone.

Like Jupiter, Saturn is believed to be a ball of gases with no solid surface. The gases that make up Saturn are mostly hydrogen and helium. There are also the ice forms of ammonia, methane and water. Further down there is liquid and then metallic hydrogen. The planet's core is made of rock and iron. Another interesting fact about Saturn is that it is the only planet that is less dense than water. Saturn would float if enough water could be found to put it in!

Only Jupiter has more moons than Saturn. Most were discovered since the start of the twenty-first century. When scientists discovered two in 2007, it brought the number of Saturn's known moons to 60. It is possible that even more will be discovered in the future.

It takes Saturn about 29.5 Earth years to revolve around the sun. As it orbits the sun, Saturn rotates on its axis very quickly: 10 hours and 39 minutes in Earth time. A combination of its speed and its gaseous composition probably accounts for the fact that Saturn appears more flattened than any other planet in our solar system. Although its winds blow even harder than Jupiter's—nearly 1,000 miles per hour—Saturn does not have the great storms that Jupiter does.

Scientists believe there are many other exciting facts are yet to be discovered about Saturn, and unmanned spacecraft are helping us learn them. The one thing we do know for sure is that there can be no life on this planet.

Saturn Discussion Questions

1. What other name is Saturn known by and why?

_____

_____

_____

2. Describe Saturn's rings.

_____

_____

_____

3. Explain why in theory Saturn could float on water.

_____

_____

_____

4. Describe Saturn's composition.

_____

_____

_____

5. How many known moons does Saturn have?

_____

_____

_____

6. Compare Saturn's day and year to Earth's day and year.

_____

_____

_____

Uranus

Uranus was named after the sky god of the ancient Greeks. It is the seventh planet from the sun and the third largest planet in the solar system. It is about four times larger than Earth and has a diameter of about 31,700 miles.

Uranus has a small rocky core of rock and iron. Above the rocky core is the mantle of mostly icy liquid hydrogen. The mantle makes up most of the planet. There is no solid surface.

The gases that make up the atmosphere of Uranus are hydrogen, helium and methane. It atmosphere is colder than that of any other planet. The cold atmosphere causes the methane to condense and form a thin cloud cover. This methane cloud is what makes Uranus looks blue-green. Although Uranus used to appear to be an almost featureless planet, stronger telescopic images show that there are seasonal changes in the atmosphere.

Like the other planets, Uranus rotates on its axis as it orbits the sun. However, there is something very unusual about the way Uranus rotates. Its tilt is so extreme that it rotates with its axis almost perpendicular to the plane of its orbit. In other words, it seems to rotate on its side—almost like a ball rolling along! Scientists are not sure why this is so. They think it might be because when Uranus was forming, a large object struck it and knocked it over on its side.

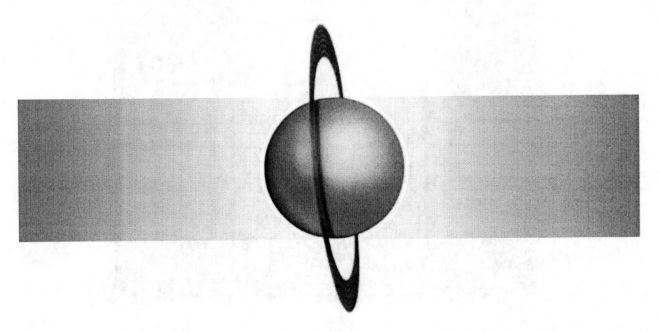

It takes Uranus about 84.1 Earth years to make one revolution around the sun. It takes about 17 hours and 14 minutes in Earth time for it to make one rotation on its axis. On Uranus each season lasts about 21 Earth years! Because of its strange tilt, the planet remains in nighttime during the winter season and in daytime in the summer season.

In 1977 astronauts discovered that Uranus also has a system of rings. Eleven have been found so far. Uranus also has 27 known moons. Many of them were discovered when *Voyager 2* observed the planet as it flew by in 1986. Although there is still a lot we don't know about this planet, astronomers learned a great deal from the pictures that *Voyager 2* sent back.

What we know for sure is that there can be no life on this icy planet!

Uranus Discussion Questions

1. Compare Uranus to the other planets in distance from the sun and size.

_____

_____

_____

2. How long are a day and a year on Uranus in Earth time?

_____

_____

_____

3. What is the make-up of Uranus?

_____

_____

_____

4. What is unusual about the way the planet rotates?

_____

_____

_____

5. What was discovered in 1977?

_____

_____

_____

6. Why can't Uranus support life?

_____

_____

_____

Neptune

Neptune was named after the mythical ancient Roman god of the seas. It is the eighth and last planet in our solar system. Neptune is so far from Earth that until recent years, we knew very little about it. *Voyager 2* flew by Neptune in 1989 and sent pictures back to Earth. Even more information was available when scientists were able to observe the planet with the Hubble telescope! The Hubble telescope is an orbiting satellite. It was launched in 1990.

About 30,775 miles in diameter, Neptune is the fourth largest planet. The composition of Neptune is similar in many ways to that of Uranus. Like that of Uranus, its atmosphere is mostly hydrogen, helium, and methane. The methane freezes in the cold atmosphere and forms an ice cloud that appears blue. Scientists think that Neptune has an extremely hot inner rocky core and a liquid mantle of water, ammonia and methane.

Neptune has raging storms and violent winds, probably caused by its heated core. As a matter of fact, Neptune has the fastest winds ever recorded in the solar system—as strong as 1,250 miles an hour. Although it is the farthest planet from the sun, scientists believe that Neptune has seasons. They based this conclusion on observations of Neptune's rotation, which were possible because of the Hubble telescope.

Neptune's day is 16 hours and 7 minutes long in Earth time. Because it is farthest from the sun, Neptune's year is longer than that of any other planet in the solar system. It takes Neptune 164.9 Earth years to make just one revolution around the sun.

From telescopic observations, astronomers have learned that Neptune has at least thirteen moons. Like the other outer planets, it also has rings. Pictures sent back from *Voyager 2* made it possible for scientists to study the faint, narrow rings. Scientists now believe there are as many as nine or more of them.

Neptune was not always called the last planet in our solar system! Pluto, which was discovered in 1846, was said to be the ninth. In 2006, however, the International Astronomical Union decided that Pluto does not fit the definition of *planet*. They said that it is a "dwarf planet." So, for now at least, we say that Neptune is the eighth and last!

There is still much we do not know about Neptune. Scientists are certain, however, that this distant planet cannot support life.

Neptune Discussion Questions

1. Compare Neptune to the other planets in size and distance from the sun.

    _____

    _____

    _____

2. Compare and contrast Neptune and Uranus.

    _____

    _____

    _____

3. How would you describe Neptune's weather?

    _____

    _____

    _____

4. How long are a day and a year on Neptune in Earth time?

    _____

    _____

    _____

5. How many known moons does Neptune have? In your opinion, why does the question say *known* moons?

    _____

    _____

    _____

6. What two objects were mentioned that helped scientists learn a lot about this very distant planet?

    _____

    _____

    _____

Comets

Comets are relatively small, icy objects that orbit around the sun in oval-shaped, or elliptical, orbits. They come in all sizes—from as small as a house to several miles across. Comets have been recorded throughout history. Many years ago when a comet was seen, people thought something terrible was happening because they didn't understand what it was. As years passed, early scientists began to understand that a comet was just a heavenly body traveling in outer space. Hundreds of comets have been recorded through the use of telescopes, but only a few have been seen by the naked eye.

There are several parts to a comet. The nucleus, or center, is composed of dirty ice, dust and gas. Surrounding the nucleus is the coma, a roundish blob of gas. The nucleus and the coma together are called the head of a comet. A comet also has a tail. In fact, there are really two tails: an ion tail, which is made of gas, and a dust tail.

Comets usually form as icy lumps in the regions beyond Neptune. Sometimes these lumps of ice are pushed towards the sun. As a comet approaches the sun, the ice begins to heat up and gases—water vapor, carbon dioxide, and ammonia—and dust form. This cloud of comet dust is called a coma. The coma is many thousands of miles wide, much larger than the comet itself.

Solar winds push the dust and gas away from the coma, causing the tail to form. The tail may be millions of miles long. It always faces away from the sun because the solar wind pushes it away. When the comet moves towards the sun, it appears to be trailing a bright tail. As the comet moves away from the sun, its tail moves in front of it.

Comets that travel around the sun in less than two hundred years are called short-period comets. An example is Halley's Comet. It comes into sight on Earth every seventy-six years. Scientists believe that Halley's Comet came from a ring of comets that orbit beyond Pluto.

Scientists believe that comets are left over from when our solar system was forming. They think that the ice crystals and dust hold lots of information about the past and that scientists would learn a lot if they could study them. In 1999 the United States launched a spacecraft called *Stardust*. Its main purpose was to make contact with the comet Wild 2 and gather dust from its trail. After a voyage of almost 3 billion miles, *Stardust* returned to Earth in 2006 with a sample of the dust. Perhaps it will help astronomers better understand our solar system's past.

Comets Discussion Questions

1. What is a comet? Name its parts.

_____

_____

_____

2. What makes a comet's tail form?

_____

_____

_____

3. From where do comets come?

_____

_____

_____

4. What is meant by a "short-period comet"? Give an example.

_____

_____

_____

5. Why are scientists interested in collecting comet dust?

_____

_____

_____

6. Explain the importance of the spacecraft *Stardust* to the study of comets.

_____

_____

_____

Asteroids

Asteroids are irregular bodies of rock and metal that orbit the sun. They are thought to be leftover material from when our solar system was first formed. They come in all shapes and sizes. They have an irregular shape because their gravity isn't strong enough to pull other material towards them.

Most asteroids are found in one area of the solar system—the area between Mars and Jupiter. In fact, this area of the solar system is sometimes called the Asteroid Belt. Millions of them orbit the sun in this belt, or span of space. However, only about 200 are more than 60 miles in diameter. It is because of the strong pull of Jupiter's gravity that these bodies do not clump together to form another planet. Scientists believe that Jupiter's great gravitational pull also protects Earth and the other inner planets from being hit by asteroids.

The first asteroid to be discovered was Ceres. By far the largest asteroid, Ceres is about 600 miles across and has a round shape like a planet. Scientists now call Ceres a dwarf planet, a term first adopted by the International Astronomical Union in 2006.

Not all asteroids travel in the Asteroid Belt. Some orbit around Jupiter. Sometimes an asteroid will jump out of its orbit and approach a planet. Some of the planets' moons were probably once asteroids that came close enough to the planet to get pulled in by the force of its gravity. Once pulled in by the planet, they orbit that planet instead of the sun.

Scientists watch asteroids that get close to the Earth very carefully. If one were to hit the Earth, it could cause great damage. It might create tidal waves or forest fires. Clouds of dust could block the sun's rays from reaching the Earth for months. This would be disastrous to life on Earth as we know it.

Even though collisions of asteroids may have helped build our planet millions of years ago, today scientists will do everything possible to keep from colliding with one!

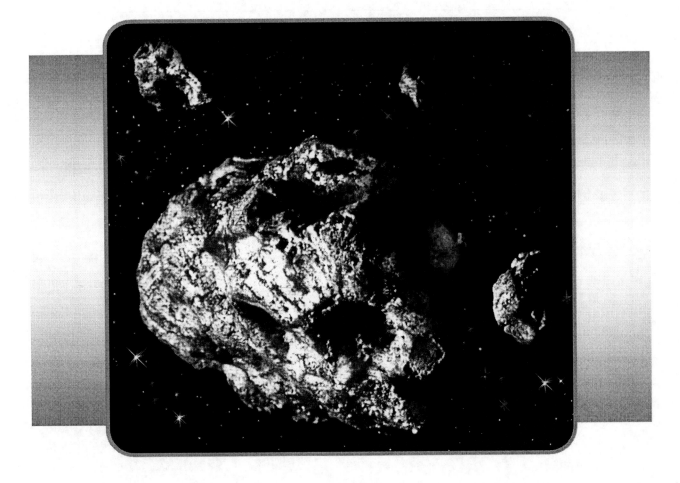

Asteroids Discussion Questions

1. What are asteroids?

   _____

   _____

   _____

2. Where can most asteroids be found?

   _____

   _____

   _____

3. Describe Ceres.

   _____

   _____

   _____

4. How does Jupiter's gravity help the inner planets?

   _____

   _____

   _____

5. What happens if an asteroid jumps orbit and gets close to a planet?

   _____

   _____

   _____

6. What might happen if an asteroid collided with Earth?

   _____

   _____

   _____

Meteoroids

Meteoroids are bits of debris, such as pieces of exploded stars, dust, rocks or metal, that travel through space. Like the other bodies in our solar system, meteoroids orbit around the sun. Most are tiny—about the size of a pebble. Many are the result of collisions between asteroids. When they collide, they break apart into many pieces. Other meteors come from the moon, from comets or from our nearest neighbor, Mars.

When a meteoroid enters Earth's atmosphere, we call it a **meteor.** Meteors travel at different speeds. The fastest ones orbit Earth at about 26 miles per second. As they travel through our atmosphere, they heat up and glow. On a clear, dark night you can usually see some meteors. People often call them "shooting stars," but they are really not stars at all. The old saying "wish upon a falling star" comes from observing these pieces of space debris falling through the Earth's atmosphere.

Over 200 tons of space debris falls each year into Earth's atmosphere. Very little of that debris ever reaches Earth's surface. Most of it burns up before it can hit the ground. If it does survive and hit the surface of Earth, the meteor is then called a **meteorite.**

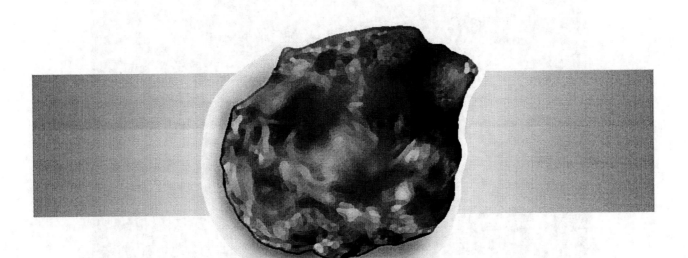

Most meteoroids come from the collision of asteroids. When they collide, pieces break off and drift through space. Eventually some of these pieces enter Earth's atmosphere and some actually fall to Earth. Many meteorites look like ordinary rocks to the untrained eye. Unless you see them fall, you probably would not know they were meteorites.

Several times during the year we have what is called a meteor shower. This happens when Earth passes through a stream of orbiting debris that broke off from a comet. During this time, many meteors can be seen in the night sky. Some meteor showers are really spectacular. In 1966, for instance, the Leonid Meteor Shower was so intense that 150,000 meteors were recorded falling in one hour. Few hit Earth, but the show was awesome.

Although most meteors burn up before becoming meteorites, some do land on Earth. An extreme example is the one that landed in Winslow, Arizona, about fifty thousand years ago. A large meteor that was moving at about 28,600 miles per hour hit the ground. Made of nickel and iron, the meteorite was about 150 feet in diameter and weighed about 300,000 tons! The tremendous explosion caused by the collision left a huge indention in the ground; that indentation is called an impact crater. The crater, called Barringer Meteorite Crater, was about 4,150 feet wide and 600 feet deep. Some scientists believe that a similar incident may have led to the disappearance of the dinosaurs millions of years ago.

Meteoroids Discussion Questions

1. What is the difference between a meteor and an asteroid?

_____

_____

_____

2. Define the terms *meteoroid, meteor* and *meteorite.*

_____

_____

_____

3. What happens when a meteor enters the Earth's atmosphere?

_____

_____

_____

4. Tell about meteor showers.

_____

_____

_____

5. Why might you not realize it if you saw a meteorite?

_____

_____

_____

6. How did most meteoroids form?

_____

_____

_____

Ready to Research

77

Paper Bag Research Pouch

Directions:

Step 1: Get a large brown paper bag. Lay it flat with the bottom facing up.

Step 2: Trim the bag on both sides about 1/4 inch from the edges.

Step 3: Open the bag and remove the sides. Lay the paper flat. You should have a very long rectangular piece.

Step 4: Divide the bag into thirds, but leave an extra 3 to 5 inches at the top. That will be the flap.

Step 5: Fold up the bottom third.

Step 6: Fold once more. The top edge should come just below the inside fold of your flap. Trim it if necessary.

Step 7: Fold down the flap.

Step 8: Tape the sides together. Do not tape down the flap!

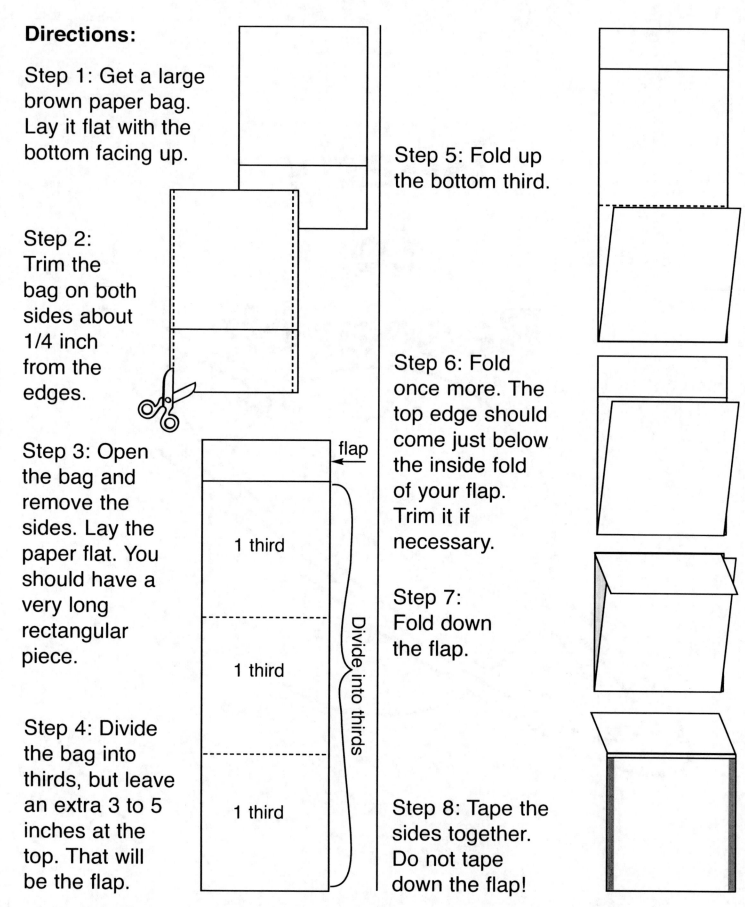

flap

1 third

1 third

1 third

Divide into thirds

Paper Bag Research Pouch (continued)

Step 9: Fold down the flap.
Cut out and glue the Our Solar System label to the flap.
Cut out and glue the My Research Pouch label on the front of the pouch.

Note: These can be found on the next page.

OUR SOLAR SYSTEM

My Research Pouch

Name: _____

Steps to Completing a Research Project

_____ 1. **Choose a topic.**

_____ 2. **Create a journal to keep up with the research process.**

_____ 3. **Collect data or research.**

    A. Use various sources as guides of where to find data.

        1. encyclopedias

        2. books

        3. magazines

        4. internet

    B. Cite the source information on the first card of each color. All information on the same color cards should belong to the same source.

    C. Decide on the categories and label the note cards. Put information about only one category on a note card. See the example on Note Cards and Organization.

_____ 4. **Develop a set of Bloom questions at each level for your topic.**

    (See Bloom section for examples.)

    A. Place each question on a separate note card.

    B. Using the collected data, answer the Bloom questions.

_____ 5. **Organize data.**

    A. Organize the cards into categories.

    B. Use the outline form to record the data retrieved from your cards.

_____ 6. **Write the paper.**

    A. Write a topic sentence.

    B. Using the outline, write the body of the paper.

    C. Have a closing sentence.

    D. Proofread and edit your paper.

    E. Have your teacher edit the paper.

    F. Write the final paper.

    G. Create a cover sheet.

_____ 7. **Create a product.**

    A. Use the Product Ideas sheet to choose a product.

    B. Use the Product Proposal sheet to plan your product.

    C. Develop the product.

    D. Evaluate the product by using the Product Evaluation form.

_____ 8. **Present your product orally.**

    A. Prepare an oral presentation for your paper and product.

    B. Have at least one visual to use in the presentation.

    C. Give the presentation to your class.

Product Ideas

diary

collection

puzzle

sculpture

cartoon

invention

play

report

model

game

photograph display

teach a lesson

want ad

TV commercial

new theory

overhead transparency

display

story

brochure

mural

greeting card

diagram

speech

book cover

audio tape

advertisement

poem

radio show

graph

map

diorama

magazine article

pop-up book

scrapbook

new product

skit

flip book

secret code

newspaper article

puppet show

time line

Product Proposal

Name of Product: _____

Supplies needed to make the product:

_____   _____

_____   _____

_____   _____

_____   _____

_____   _____

Steps needed to make the product:

1._____

2._____

3._____

4._____

5._____

6._____

Did you have any problems?

_____

_____

_____

What could you do differently to make the product better?

_____

_____

Product Evaluation

Are you pleased with your product? Why or why not?

_____

_____

_____

Do you think your product reflects your research? How?

_____

_____

_____

_____

If you scored your product, 1 being the lowest and 10 being the highest, what score would you give it? Circle one.

1   2   3   4   5   6   7   8   9   10

Give some reasons why you scored your product as you did.

_____

_____

_____

_____

Did you enjoy making your product? Why or why not?

_____

_____

_____

_____

Oral Presentation Tips

1. Know your topic and material well.

2. Be organized. Have your materials and information ready to use in your presentation.

3. Practice your presentation:

    • Do not read your presentation.

    • Give your presentation to anyone who will listen. Practice with your parents, your siblings, even your pets. The more often you give the presentation, the better and more comfortable you will become.

4. Make good eye contact with your audience.

5. Stand up straight, move a little, and don't stand in a frozen stance.

6. Use an oral presentation format:

    • Introduce your topic.

    • Explain each point you are trying to make.

    • Summarize your presentation with one or two sentences.

    • Ask if there are any questions.

7. Never turn your back on the audience.

8. Make sure your audience can hear you clearly.

    • Speak slowly so everyone can understand you.

Extension Activities

What Does It Take to Be an Astronaut?

Make a list of character traits that you think are necessary to be an astronaut.

_____

_____

_____

_____

_____

_____

_____

_____

Now tell why you think you would or would not make a good astronaut.

_____

_____

_____

_____

_____

_____

_____

_____

_____

_____

_____

A New Planet

Imagine that you have discovered a new planet. Describe it, including its size, composition, special characteristics, moons, etc. Will there be life on your planet? Name your new planet.

_____

_____

_____

_____

_____

_____

_____

_____

_____

_____

_____

_____

Illustrate your planet.

Not Good Enough!
Research and find out why scientists decided that Pluto is not a planet.

What a Trip!
Suppose you could visit any planet in the solar system. Which would you visit and why? Tell about your visit to the planet.

It's a Big One!
Write a newspaper report about a giant asteroid that is headed to Earth. Predict what will happen if it hits.

A World Without Sun
Suppose the sun died. Write about what would happen to the solar system.

Create a Model
Create a model of our solar system.

A Collage
Make a collage of all eight planets with the sun being in the center.

A Brochure
Create a fact file about the planets.

Choose Me!
Write a letter to NASA to convince them that you should be on the first manned mission to Mars.

Bibliography

Bradley, Franklyn. *The Planets in Our Solar System*. New York: HarperCollins Publishers, 1981.

Cole, Joanna. *The Magic School Bus Lost in the Solar System.* New York: Scholastic Inc., 1990.

Freeman, Mae and Ira Freeman. *The Sun, the Moon, and the Stars*. New York: Random House, 1979.

Goldstein, Margaret J. *The Solar System*. Minneapolis: Lerner Publications, 2003.

Muirden, James. *Seeing Stars.* Cambridge, Massachusetts: Candlewick Press, 1998.

Rabe, Tish. *There's No Place Like Space*. New York: Random House, 1999.

Simon, Seymor. *Comets, Meteors, and Asteroids*. New York: Mulberry Paperback Books, 1994.

——. *Stars.* New York: Mulberry Paperback Books, 1986.

"Solar System". 1/23/2007. http://www.bbc.co.uk/science/space/solarsystem/

Stark, Rebecca. *Thinking About Science: Our Solar System*. Hawthorne, NJ: Educational Impressions, Inc., 2000.

Zim, Herbert. *Comets*. New York William Morrow and Company, 1957.